Collecting
BURLEIC

A photographic guide to the Art Deco jugs and fancies of Burgess and Leigh

Written and researched by
ELIZABETH R. COUPE

Designed, Typeset and Published by Letterbox Publishing
Unit 1a Rural Industries, John O'Gaunt, Melton Mowbray, Leicestershire LE14 2RE.
Telephone 01664 454114 Fax 01664 454115.

Photographs by Barry Coupe or reproduced by kind permission.

Front and Back Cover Illustrations by Deborah Hinks.

ISBN 0 9532462 7 2

Foreword

I am delighted that Elizabeth Coupe has followed up her guide to the tableware designs of Harold Bennett, with this companion volume which includes yellow glaze flower jugs, already quite well known to collectors, as well as Dickens and Shakespeare characters, pieces commemorative of Sir Winston Churchill and other wartime leaders and other fancy items.

These were all modelled by Ernest Bailey who had a particular aptitude for figure modelling as evidenced by his likeness of Churchill and the Dickens characters. While Harold Bennett was responsible for the decoration this was in many cases indicated by the nature of the piece.

The flower jugs, of which more than two dozen were modelled, were very popular throughout the 1930's aided materially by the bright yellow glaze developed by our works manager Harold Lowe. The most popular were depicting birds and animals which usually formed the handle as with parrot, squirrel, and kingfisher.

There was considerable demand for Pied Piper and Harvest, a sheaf of corn. Such was their success that it necessitated the building of two new casting shops and a large new decorating shop.

Edmund Leigh

Chairman - Burgess & Leigh Ltd.

3

About the Author

*A*lthough we have known the author for only a few years, it became immediately apparent that she had a great passion for Art Deco ceramics. Elizabeth's willingness to share her knowledge of ceramics with warmth and conviction is a valuable asset. It is this desire to share her love of Burleigh ware with others, coupled with many requests for a Guide to their jugs, that has compelled her to write this, her second book.

Born in Northallerton, Yorkshire, she moved to Lincoln in 1960 and has remained there ever since. Elizabeth spent some thirty years of her working life teaching, mostly at a local Comprehensive School. She has two daughters and two grandsons and has been married for thirty two years.

Having had a keen interest in ceramics for many years, Elizabeth's hobby led her to begin dealing at the Hemswell Antiques Centres in 1991. Four years later, both she and her husband took early retirement from teaching and now run a successful business.

By producing this follow-up colourful insight into the work of Burgess and Leigh, the author hopes to once again convert you, the reader, into an equally avid follower of their much-loved jugs and vases.

KEVIN and JULIE GLOVER

Acknowledgments

I would like to thank the following for their help and support in the production of this guide.

My sincerest thanks again go to the Chairman of Burgess and Leigh, Mr. Edmund Leigh, who has kindly supplied me with valuable information and assistance and agreed to write the Foreword for this book. Also I wish to thank his brother, Mr. Barry Leigh and his charming wife, who not only spoke to me of their memories of the factory but also brought information to me in Lincoln without which it would have been impossible for me to write this guide as it stands.

Again I am indebted to my husband, Barry, for the majority of the photographs included in the guide and for his continued patience and unstinting support and encouragement. Grateful thanks must also go to my daughters, Deborah for her splendid designs on the cover of this guide and Claire for her help with the computer.

Very special thanks must go to Lesley and Bill Jackson who have not only provided the Price Guide and other useful information but have also allowed their superb collection of yellow jugs to be photographed, whilst providing us with true Yorkshire hospitality.

For his continued encouragement and support, as well as his hard work in the production and publishing of this book, I would like to thank my good friend Kevin Glover, whose professional skills are proving indispensable. Thanks, too, to his wife, Julie, for her continued guidance and patience.

My parents, John and Margaret Balch, deserve special thanks, for their continued assistance, financial and otherwise.

Trish and Alan Patterson, too, merit special thanks for allowing us to photograph their excellent collection of Burleigh Ware, for their kindness to my husband and myself on our visit to them and for the help with the prices.

Finally, for additional photographs and advice I must thank Martin Lister and Jerry Moeran.

Frederick Burgess and the Leigh family

1851

FREDERICK RATHBONE
BURGESS
(Founder)

WILLIAM
LEIGH
(Founder)

EDMUND
LEIGH, J.P.
(First Chairman)

A.KINGSLEY
LEIGH

E.DENIS
LEIGH

1951

R.E.K
LEIGH

D.B
LEIGH

Reproduced from the Centenary Publication of 1951
Courtesy of Mr. E. Leigh

Contents

Introduction

S ince the publication of the Guide to the Art Deco Tablewares from Burgess and Leigh, I have received many requests to produce a similar guide to the factory's other 1930's products.

A special interest has been shown in the yellow glazed flower jugs, which are favourites with collectors.

As a result, I again solicited the help of the Chairman of the firm, Mr. Edmund Leigh. Both he and his brother, Mr. D. B Leigh, have been most supportive and provided me with vital information.

Whilst the guide concentrates mainly on the yellow glazed flower jugs of the 1930's, I have also included the more conventional Alcock jugs, and the character and bird jugs from the 1940's and 1950's, all modelled by Ernest Bailey.

Throughout its history, Burgess and Leigh has moved with the times and its products have much to offer the Art Deco collector. As well as the flower jugs, many wonderful "lozenge" jugs, vases, baskets, wall pockets and plaques etc. were made in the Art Deco style.

Examples of these have also been included.

Photographs of the Factory

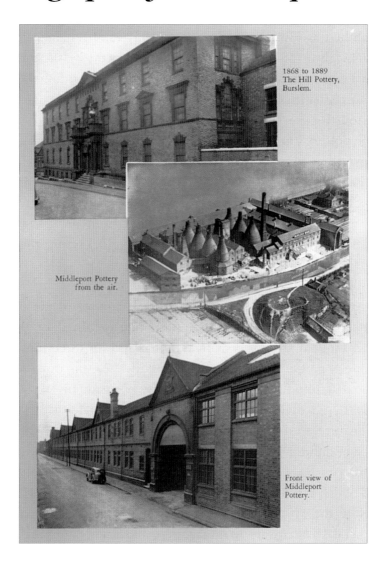

a) 1868 to 1889, the Hill Pottery, Burslem
b) Middleport Pottery from the air   c) Front view of Middleport Pottery
Reproduced from the Centenary Publication of 1951
Courtesy of Mr. E. Leigh

A Brief History of the Factory

Established as Hulme and Booth in 1851, and renamed Burgess and Leigh in 1877, the firm is still being run by the family of William Leigh, one of the founders of the pottery. Edmund Leigh, the present Chairman of the company, is William's Great Grandson and the fourth generation in the family business.

The pottery's first home was at the Central Pottery, Burslem, but after expansion, soon moved to the Hill Pottery. When this factory also became too small, a new factory was built at Middleport, Burslem, at the side of the Trent and Mersey Canal. The pottery was opened in 1889, and the firm still operates from here. Only one disused bottle oven still remains from the original seven, the firing now being done by gas fired kilns.

William Leigh died in 1889 and Frederick Burgess in 1898, so their two sons, Edmund and Richard, took control of the pottery. When Richard died in 1912, Edmund took charge. In 1919, the firm became a Limited Company with Edmund and his three sons acting as first directors. On the death of Edmund in 1924, the three remaining directors continued and developed the business. In 1954 Arthur Kingsley Leigh died after running the company for thirty years. Denis, his brother, became Chairman until his death in 1968. Since this time, Edmund Leigh, the present Chairman, with his brother Barry, has run the company. Their children are also involved in the business which is still very much a family affair.

Before the First World War, the firm was described as a Toilet and General Earthenware Manufacturers and toilet wares accounted for half the output of the factory. In the early 1920's, with the decline in the toilet ware trade, additional tea and dinner wares were introduced. Only a short time later, the fashion for brightly coloured, on glaze decoration developed and this continued throughout the 1930's.

This was a profitable time for Burgess and Leigh. The introduction of the new Art Deco shapes on table wares with their handpainting and enamelling, proved popular with the public. It was at this time too, that the firm developed the ranges that are now regarded as some of its most sought-after wares – the yellow flower jugs, Art Deco vases, fancy wares and character jugs.

The Second World War, with its severe restrictions on productions of all kinds, banned the sale of decorated wares in the United Kingdom and limited output to "Utility" ranges. Any decorated wares could be exported to alleviate the shortage of foreign money. The company took advantage of this and still exports a great deal of its products.

In the 1950's, when decorated wares could again be produced, the 1930's methods were too expensive, so lithograph and screen printing transfers were successfully introduced. By the 1960's, contemporary designs were based on the traditional methods of underglaze printing and banding and today the underglaze patterns, Willow, Asiatic Pheasant, Calico etc. form the bulk of the firm's product range which is exported all over the world.

Inside the Factory

a) *Plate making on semi-automatic machines*   b) *A modern Casting Shop*
c) *Burleigh Ware ready for Export*   d) *Continuous firing Glost Oven*
Reproduced from the Centenary Publication of 1951
Courtesy of Mr. E. Leigh

Yellow Flower Jugs

Some of the most collectable ceramics from the 1930's are the eye catching yellow flower jugs from the firm of Burgess and Leigh. Popular then, as they are today, these jugs were modelled by Ernest Tansley Bailey. Bailey joined the firm in 1925 and became apprenticed to the Chief Modeller, Charles Wilkes. He was to remain with the factory, later as Chief Modeller himself, until his retirement in 1980. During the Second World War, Bailey served in the Navy, having been called up in 1942 He was demobbed in 1946. Not only are we indebted to Ernest Bailey for the yellow flower jugs but also for other familiar collectables from this factory, namely Art Deco vases and jugs, Fancy wares and character jugs. The wonderful table-wares too, which have been dealt with in our other guide, were modelled by Bailey.

The man responsible for the designs on Bailey's shapes was the watercolour artist, Harold Bennett. He joined Burgess and Leigh in 1929 to assist the ageing Art Director, 'Designer Leigh', thus named to avoid confusion with the owners. Charlotte Rhead was employed at the factory at this time and it seems that she and Bennett did not have a particularly good relationship. Perhaps the fact that the post of Art Director was in the offing, due to the imminent retirement of 'Designer Leigh', caused some problems. In any event, Charlotte left the factory in 1931 and Harold Bennett eventually became Art Director and Chief Designer. Bennett was a wonderful artist with a passion for trees and is known to have had two landscapes exhibited at the Royal Academy in 1945.

These, then, are two of the men primarily responsible for the famous Burleigh jugs. The man who developed the beautiful primrose glaze for the jugs was named Harold Lowe. He added antimony, a metallic element into his glaze to achieve this colour and thus created a best seller for the firm, one which was to be copied by many other factories.

The jugs produced with the yellow glaze were modelled between 1931 and 1938 and sold until 1954. They were hugely popular at the time, mainly with the middle market and made in several colourways. It seems that the major stores at the time demanded different designs from their competitors. The jugs retailed through such stores as Harrod's, Liberty and Selfridge's. The factory employed three reps in the UK at this time. These men had to ensure orders for at least twelve products of the same mould before production could take place. By 1951, the Centenary of Burgess and Leigh, over one quarter of a million jugs had been sold. The jugs were free hand painted with black stitch edges – 'Sunshine edges' as Bennett called them. In the early 1930's one hundred paintresses were employed at the factory from a workforce of four hundred and fifty. Each colourway was given a different pattern number which often appears hand written on the base of the jug.

The handles on the jugs were largely modelled in the shape of a bird, an animal or a human figure, with complementary designs on the body. Some were produced in large numbers – the bulk lines; Parrot, Squirrel, Dragon, Kingfisher, Butterflies, Harvest, Pied Piper. Others were produced in only limited numbers and are highly sought after today. Recently it was reported that a Guards jug changed hands for £3,000. The range also included jugs with flowers on the handle. The Garden and Lupin jugs fall into this category. Sometimes a different glaze was used for the jugs in this series, e.g. green or beige. These do not appear to be as sought after as those in yellow. It seems also, that pink and blue colourways were not as popular as brighter colours and these are therefore less common. The jugs were of various shapes as can be seen in the photographic guide but although colours may differ, the shape for each subject remains the same. Occasionally unpainted yellow jugs appear on the market. These unfinished products are presumably seconds since the firm insists on a high standard for all their products, irrespective of price. These jugs, usually with a visible flaw must have somehow found their way out of the factory.

So far, we have discovered 27 yellow jugs. There may be others in the series which have escaped us. I would be grateful for any information from readers regarding these.

Below is a list of known jugs with a brief description.

1. SQUIRREL 1931. 8-inches. On this first jug in the series, a squirrel forms the handle. The main body has moulded acorns near the spout and most are decorated with a tree or falling leaves. This was one of the most popular jugs and has been seen in more than ten colourways, although the squirrel itself is usually brown.

2. PARROT 1931. Appearing in countless colourways, this jug with a parrot forming the handle, came in two sizes – 8-inches and 3-inches. The parrot is sitting on the branch of a bamboo, with its beak overhanging the rim of the jug. Whilst the decoration on the jugs was in many different colours, all show a butterfly and a large bamboo leaf. There is also a rare two handled Parrot jug.

3. DRAGON 1931. Produced in two sizes, 10-inches and 8-inches, the dragon's tail makes up the handle of this jug, with the rest of its body moulded on to the jug itself. Again designed in a variety of colourways, this popular jug may be quite simply painted or have much more detail, especially on the face. Prices will be affected accordingly.

4. KINGFISHER 1931. The Kingfisher jug came in three sizes, 10-inches, 8-inches and 3-inches. Having a plainer handle than its predecessors, the bird's tail is at the base, with the rest of the bird appearing to fly onto the jug to catch the fish in his beak. Blue, green, black, orange and brown kingfishers have been noted and no doubt there are more.

5. FLAMINGO 1932. At 9.5-inches tall, this straighter, slimmer jug is decorated on the body with a flamingo swooping down towards the bottom of the jug, which has a triangular handle with a flower at its top. The bird is painted in many different colours, the most popular being pink, blue or orange.

6. BUTTERFLY 1933. Butterflies and flowers adorn the handle and main body of this charming jug. At the standard size of 8-inches, this jug often appears with the butterflies edged in black.

7. HARVEST 1933. Shaped like a sheaf of corn with a rabbit nestling in its stalks, this jug is usually found in two colourways. The flowers in either orange, to represent poppies, or blue, for cornflowers. This jug also came in two sizes – 7.5-inches and 5.5-inches.

8. PIED PIPER 1933. The first of the jugs to have a human figure moulded as the handle, the Pied Piper entices the rats to follow him up the handle of the jug. Hamelin, with its tall towers, can be seen on the jug itself. Produced in many designs, the Pied Piper is seen in a variety of differently coloured clothes, usually sporting a spotted shirt. Those with purple hats seem to be most sought after. Sometimes the rats appear in silhouette. The standard size for this jug is 8.5-inches.

9. HIGHWAYMAN 1933. Following the lines of the Pied Piper, the Highwayman, reputedly Dick Turpin, is seen, pistol at the ready, aiming at the coach and horses galloping across the jug. Wearing hat, cape, boots etc., he looks a formidable character. Often orange with a black or green cape, there are many other colourways. Normally this jug is some 8-inches tall but it is believed that a smaller one was produced.

10. GUARDS 1933. Two varieties of this rare 8-inch jug are known. One with a sentry box on the back and soldiers on the front. The other with Guards marching around the whole jug. The records of the factory reveal that this jug was produced for only a short time as it was not popular. Colourways seen for this jug are black trousers with orange stripe, green trousers with black stripe and yellow trousers with black stripe Are there any more?

11. SHIP 1934. Another very rare jug, of which I have only seen pictures, was modelled as a ship in full sail. Having an ear shaped handle, it came in three sizes.

12. MONKEY AND CAT 1934. Believed to be based on the story of the spiteful monkey who tried to hold the cat's paw in the fire, this jug is rare. Taller than most at 10-inches, the monkey forms the handle, whilst the cat, usually painted black, stands before a fire holding up his paw

13. PHEASANT 1936. With a covering of bracken leaves on the jug and a pheasant as the handle, this jug came in one size – 7.5-inches and several colourways.

14. FOX AND STORK. The date of this jug is unknown. Some consider the subject to be a wolf rather than a fox, others that it is based on Aesop's fable. The handle is modelled as the stork with its beak resting on the rim of the jug, the fox, tongue extended in anticipation, sits longingly on the side of the jug. The jug is 9.5-inches high.

15. KANGAROO. Possibly produced primarily for the Australian market, the Kangaroo came in two sizes – 7.5-inches and 10-inches. The kangaroos are on the body of this rare jug. The handle is a branch of a flowering tree.

16. HONEYCOMB. At 8-and-a-half inches this jug is often known as Bees. It was produced to give the surface of the jug a honeycombed effect with bees superimposed on its surface. The bees are usually orange and black with white wings.

17. GARDEN. This pretty jug, with a handle of flowers, is decorated with a rock garden scene and is 7.5-inches high. The flowers on the handle are usually in the blue or red colourway.

18. BUDGERIGAR 1938. The Budgerigar jug is modelled in a more conical shape. It has a budgerigar sitting inside the handle, and another bird flying towards it across the jug. The budgerigar is usually in shades of blue on this rare jug which stands at 8-inches.

19. LUPIN. Only 6-inches high, the Lupin jug has a thick handle in the shape of a lupin flower and the body is decorated with another lupin and leaves. In most cases the handle is pink.

20. BIRD OF PARADISE. A tall jug at 10-inches, the handle formed as a two branched tree opening up to leaves on the jug, the Bird of Paradise can also be found as a small 3-inch jug. A small bird with a long tail sits at the top of the handle.

21. STOAT. This jug goes by many names, and no-one seems to know exactly what it is meant to represent. The black tip on the tail would suggest that it could be a stoat. It is a conical jug with a handle reminiscent of that on the Squirrel jug and is decorated on its upper half with corn stalks. Stoat was made in two sizes, 7-inches and 4-inches.

22. FOX 1934. The tail of the fox forms the handle of this small 6-inch jug. The fox lies down at the base of the jug which is decorated with flowers.

23. GOLFER 1934. In this year the first of the sportsmen jug was modelled. This was the Golfer, 8-inches high and also produced in white. Featuring a golfer in full swing as the handle with a golf course decorating the jug. In chequered or plain trousers, the jug is in many colourways and is keenly collected. A smaller golfing jug has also been noted.

24. CRICKETER 1935. Perhaps modelled on Don Bradman, the Cricketer jug, also made in white, is the second sportsman jug in the series. The handle beautifully formed as a cricketer with pads and cap and the main jug showing the bat and pavilion, makes this 8-inch jug a winner.

25. TENNIS PLAYER 1936. A female tennis player makes up the handle of this, the third and final jug in the series. Painted in a striped or plain costume, the Tennis Player is also seen in white and is popular with collectors. The design on the jug shows a racket, ball and net. There are rumours that a Footballer jug was made, based on Sir Stanley Matthews and possibly a Swimmer but there is, as yet, no evidence.

26. PIXIE 1938. An unusual jug, surrounded by mushrooms or toadstools and the handle formed as a green pixie or goblin crouching down. It appears in at least three colourways and is quite rare.

27. GRAPES 1938. Modelled to give the appearance of a large bunch of grapes, this strange jug can be found in green and burgundy as well as in the yellow glaze.

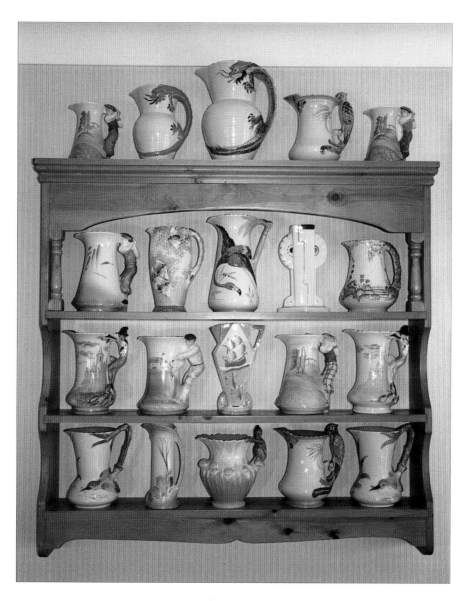

A superb collection of Burleigh Jugs.

Courtesy of L & W Jackson

19

Art Deco Jugs and Vases

In the 1930's, Burgess and Leigh produced a range of jugs and vases in the high Art Deco style. Some of the most interesting are the Double Diamond and Lozenge shaped pieces. Having a yellow glaze, they are hand painted with geometric patterns, swans, galleons, leaping gazelles etc. and are highly sought after today

A few examples of this range are listed below and included in the photographic guide. Most are 8-inches high.

LOZENGE GALLEON JUG This slim jug is diamond shaped with a triangular handle, moulded as a seascape, the top half shows a galleon, whilst underneath, below the waves, are two fish.

DOUBLE DIAMOND LOZENGE VASE Available in two sizes, 8.5-inches and 7.5-inches, this vase appears as twin vases joined together. Often seen decorated with swans and trees it can also be found with geometric patterns.

TRUMPET SHAPED JUG There is a band of brown at the top and bottom of this jug which has an ear-shaped handle. Examples have been seen with falling leaves or the sun's rays.

OVOID VASE This is an oval flat vase with angular pieces to the top. It has been seen with trees or leaves.

LOVE-BIRDS Affectionately known as Love-birds, this vase has a wavy rim and shows two colourful birds sitting closely together on a branch. Inners from these vases are often missing.

RIBBED JUG The ribbed jug comes in many different designs and colours and has a rectangular handle. It is so called because most of its surface is covered in ridges.

LEAPING GAZELLES Having an oval body and a triangular spout, this stunning jug is modelled with two gazelles, one above the other.

TOTEM POLE VASE This is the name often given to this unusual vase. It has a diamond shaped base, a rectangular main body and two semi-circular projections at the top.

SLIM JUG The body of this jug is only 2.5-inches wide. It has been seen with a tree and crocuses near the base or a sunrise.

TRIANGULAR JUG This jug is of a triangular shape and has a triangular handle. It is painted with stylised flowers and leaves.

Another superb set of Burleigh Jugs. *Courtesy of L & W Jackson*

Fancy Wares and Bird Jugs

The 1930's saw many factories producing what are often referred to as Fancy Wares or Novelties. Burgess and Leigh were no exception. Alongside the jugs, they made matching wall plaques and inventive containers for flowers. These came in the form of baskets with bamboo handles, tree trunk shaped vases, hat shaped vases, wall pockets, posy troughs, some formed as rings, supporting birds or animals, others moulded in relief. The famous Indian in his canoe comes from this factory. Tea sets were produced which had small jugs, similar to the large flower jugs, in such patterns as Thistle, Pansy and Strawberry.

BIRD JUGS Towards the end of 1955, a series of small bird jugs was modelled by Bailey. These jugs were also glazed in primrose yellow and beautifully hand painted. There were five birds in the range, each with its beak forming the spout of the jug. The first jug was Kingfisher, in November, followed by Wren, Blue Tit, Bullfinch and Budgerigar in December. A model of a large Turkey has been noted but it is not believed to be part of this series.

PRICE RANGE: £150 to £200   *Courtesy of A & P Patterson*

Samuel Alcock Reproduction Jugs

The firm of Samuel Alcock ceased production at the Hill Pottery in the 1860's. After its closure, Burgess and Leigh purchased some moulds from Alcock's included in which were moulds for five jugs.

Arms of All Nations
Feeding Time
Bulrush
Babes in the Wood
Gypsy Encampment

Previously it had been thought that the jug, Sally in Our Alley, was one of the original moulds but Mr Leigh suggests that Ernest Bailey modelled this himself from a pattern of a jug produced by the firm some twenty years earlier. He remembers as a boy that there were two vases of this pattern on his bedroom mantlepiece. Between the years, 1930 and 1950, Sally and Feeding Time were reproduced fully hand painted. Other jugs were newly modelled by Bailey to add to the series. Most of these jugs have a verse or brief description underneath. These traditional jugs were sold to more conventional customers. The publication produced by the factory for its Centenary in 1951, shows a picture of two jugs, Feeding Time and Arms of All Nations, and describes them as still "Best Sellers". The new jugs are listed. There may be more!

Sally in Our Alley
The Village Blacksmith
Stocks
Nell Gwyn
The Runaway Marriage

Between 1965 and 1980, Feeding Time, Bulrush, Babes in the Wood and Gypsy Encampment were produced with a blue shaded treatment. A limited number were also made with pink shading.

Dickens Character Jugs

The first series of character jugs manufactured by Burgess and Leigh was the Dickens Series. These jugs were in general line until 1985 and were fully hand painted. In August 1941, Bailey produced the first jug – Charles Dickens and followed this with five characters from Dickens' novels.

Pickwick	**Tony Weller**
Pecksniff	**Sairey Gamp**
Micawber	

Later, probably 1945-6, a further five jugs were added to the range.

Scrooge	**Nicholas Nickelby**
Oliver Twist	**Sam Weller**
Daniel Peggotty	

It seems that Oliver and Sairey were dropped from the line early on and replaced by Scrooge and Nickleby, thus making the former rare and valuable. **Mrs Bardell** was also modelled but was never fully put into production.

The most popular jugs which formed the 'bulk line' were Pickwick, Pecksniff, Micawber, Sam and Tony Weller, Nicholas Nickleby, Daniel Peggotty and Scrooge.

Charles Dickens
PRICE RANGE: £30 to £50
Courtesy of A & P Patterson

Shakespeare Character Jugs

In April 1950 a character jug of William Shakespeare was modelled. This was a large jug, being slightly over 6-inches in height and it took five weeks of modelling time. Subsequently, a further fourteen small jugs were planned to make up the series but it would seem that not all went into mass production. Marketed until 1985, all hand painted, the following eight jugs were the only ones made in any quantity.

Wolsey	**Shylock**
Macbeth	**Falstaff**
Touchstone	**Romeo**
Portia	**Midsummer Night's Dream**

The firm still has moulds for the six other jugs in the series. Occasionally an odd one turns up, perhaps a prototype, but if produced at all they were done so in very limited numbers. They are as follows:

Caesar
Hamlet
Juliet
Malvolio
Othello
Ophelia

William Shakespeare
PRICE RANGE: £30 to £50
Courtesy of A & P Patterson

Wartime Leaders

Perhaps the most famous of all Burleigh character jugs are those modelled on **Winston Churchill**. There were three of these, all made in 1941 and produced, hand painted, during the Second World War. The most successful of these was the Victory Jug which shows a squat figure of Churchill making the V-sign. A letter V in morse code is on the base. Mr. Leigh believes that this was the last of the three to be made. The first, a John Bull jug, entitled Bulldogs, was modelled in February. Twice as large as the Victory jug, it shows a full size figure of Churchill with a bulldog at his feet and a Union Jack. The second, modelled in July, in two sizes, depicts the leader in what appears to be a naval uniform, with a small cigar butt in his mouth. Mr. Leigh suggests "The uniform Churchill is shown as wearing is not clear. He was never in the Navy and while he may possibly have had some sort of naval uniform when First Lord of the Admiralty, any photos I have seen for subsequent First Lords show them in civilian dress. On the other hand he had frequently worn, and was very proud of the uniform of an older brother of Trinity House, the organisation which looked after our lighthouses. I think, therefore, this is probably what the blue uniform was."

Courtesy of Mr E Leigh

Others

Jugs of other wartime leaders were also made at this time. In October 1940, a Chamberlain jug was modelled but it is not known if it was ever put into production in any significant numbers. A prototype model of Sir Stafford Cripps was made in the same style as the squat Churchill jug the following year and in July 1941, a Jan Smuts prototype was also made. There were copyright problems with this, so again few were produced. In November 1941 Stalin was modelled but was unpopular and had only a short run. In March 1942 a 3-inch jug of General MacArthur was made and sold in the United States.

Bailey also modelled Beefeater and Chelsea Pensioner in the late 1940's and in 1953, three Coronation jugs were designed. One in Alcock style, one modelled as the Queen sitting on the Coronation throne, and one with the Queen seated on horseback.

The majority of all jugs were manufactured in the 1950's. Wartime restrictions precluded painting for the local economy from 1942 to 1953, so most of the jugs were sent to the U.S. before 1953. Only a few white jugs were made and by 1985 all jugs had been discontinued as they were no longer selling in sufficient numbers and were costly to produce. Half the painter's time was spent on the faces. Mary Harper, a worker-foreman at Burgess and Leigh, was one of the main paintresses on the character jugs. Like many workers at the factory, Mary was a loyal employee. Joining the staff in about 1906, she continued working until the age of seventy five years, retiring in 1968. Happily she lived on for many years after retirement.

After the discontinuation, those bisque jugs that were left in stock were sprayed in blue shades and sold off at reduced prices in 1986-7.

SQUIRREL

PRICE RANGE: £75 to £120

Courtesy of L & W Jackson

PARROT (7017)

PRICE RANGE: £75 to £125

Courtesy of L & W Jackson

DRAGON (5118)

PRICE RANGE: Small £80 to £130   Large £150 to £250

Courtesy of L & W Jackson

KINGFISHER (5103)

PRICE RANGE: Small £80 to £130   Large £125 to £225

Courtesy of L & W Jackson

FLAMINGO (5094)

PRICE RANGE: £150 to £275

Courtesy of L & W Jackson

BUTTERFLIES (7022)

PRICE RANGE: £125 *to* £225

Courtesy of L & W Jackson

HARVEST (5064)

PRICE RANGE: Large £60 to £100

Courtesy of B & E Coupe

PIED PIPER (5984)

PRICE RANGE: £125 to £175

Courtesy of L & W Jackson

HIGHWAYMAN (5065)

PRICE RANGE: £225 to £350

Courtesy of L & W Jackson

MONKEY AND CAT

PRICE RANGE: *£800 to £1000*

Courtesy of J Moeran

GUARDS (5061)

PRICE RANGE: £1750 to £3000

Courtesy of L & W Jackson

GUARDS (5061)

PRICE RANGE: £1750 to £3000

Courtesy of L & W Jackson

PHEASANT (5624)

PRICE RANGE: £225 to £300

Courtesy of L & W Jackson

FOX AND STORK (5162)

PRICE RANGE: £175 to £275

Courtesy of L & W Jackson

KANGAROO (4911)

PRICE RANGE: *Large £500 to £600   Small £350 to £450*

Courtesy of L & W Jackson

HONEYCOMB (5418)

PRICE RANGE: £275 to £400

Courtesy of L & W Jackson

GARDEN (5125)

PRICE RANGE: £150 to £200

Courtesy of D Bennett

BUDGERIGAR (6049)

PRICE RANGE: £500 to £900

Courtesy of L & W Jackson

LUPIN

PRICE RANGE: £100 to £175

Courtesy of A & P Patterson

BIRD OF PARADISE

PRICE RANGE: £175 to £275

Courtesy of J Moeran

STOAT

PRICE RANGE: £200 to £250

Courtesy of A & P Patterson

FOX

PRICE RANGE: £200 to £275

Courtesy of A & P Patterson

GOLFER

PRICE RANGE: £600 to £1000

Courtesy of L & W Jackson

CRICKETER

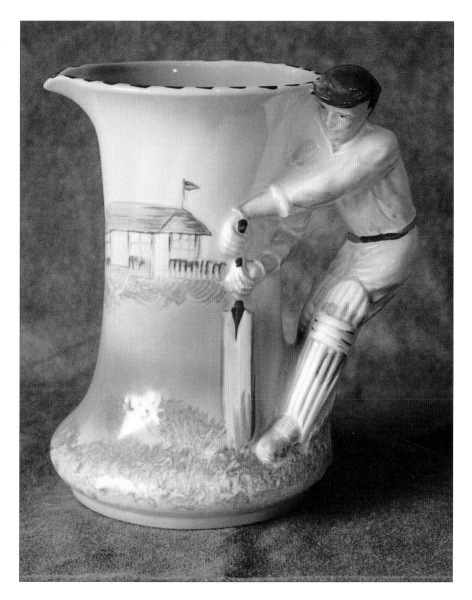

PRICE RANGE: £600 to £1500

Courtesy of L & W Jackson

TENNIS PLAYER (5329)

PRICE RANGE: £1250 to £2000

Courtesy of L & W Jackson

PIXIE (6431)

PRICE RANGE: £200 to £375

Courtesy of D Bennett

GRAPES (6375)

PRICE RANGE: £100 to £175

Courtesy of K & J Glover

SHIP

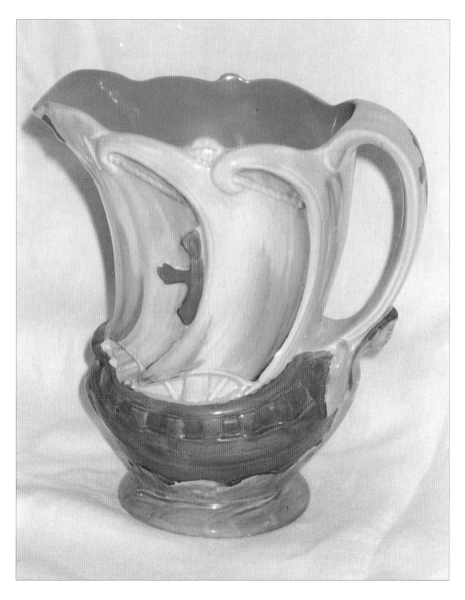

PRICE RANGE: £400 to £600

Courtesy of S & M Lister

LOZENGE JUGS

GALLEON & FISHES (5165)
PRICE RANGE: £350 to £500

Left: Courtesy of L & W Jackson
Right: Courtesy of G & M Wiles

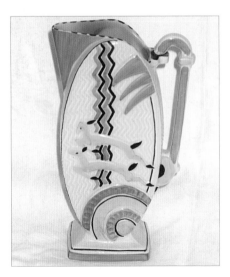 

LEAPING GAZELLES
PRICE RANGE: £400 to £550

Left: Courtesy of S & M Lister
Right: Courtesy of J Moeran

ART DECO JUGS

RIBBED JUGS (6640)
PRICE RANGE: £75 to £125

Left: Courtesy of R Jackson
Right: Courtesy of G & M Wiles

TRUMPET SHAPED JUG
PRICE RANGE: £100 to £150
Courtesy of L & W Jackson

TRIANGULAR JUG
PRICE RANGE: £200 to £300
Courtesy of S & M Lister

ART DECO VASES

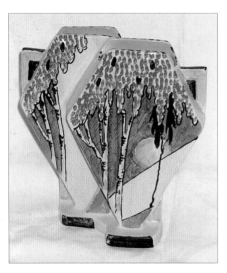 

DOUBLE LOZENGE VASES
PRICE RANGE: £500 to £700

Left: Courtesy of S & M Lister
Right: Courtesy of J Moeran

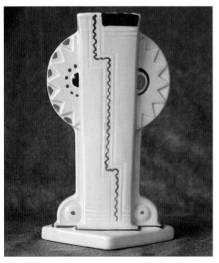 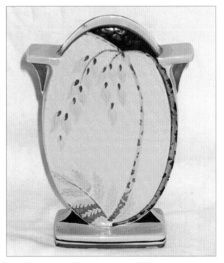

TOTEM VASE (5198)
PRICE RANGE: £400 to £500
Courtesy of L & W Jackson

OVOID VASE
PRICE RANGE: £300 to £375
Courtesy of S & M Lister

ART DECO VASES/JUGS

LOVEBIRDS
PRICE RANGE: £300 to £450

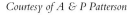

Courtesy of A & P Patterson

SLIM JUG (5690)
PRICE RANGE: £125 to £175
Courtesy of L & W Jackson

TWIN PARROTS
PRICE RANGE: £1200 to £2000
Courtesy of S & M Lister

FANCY WARES

PRICE RANGE: £40 to £60

PRICE RANGE: £75 to £100   *Whole page courtesy of A & P Patterson*

PRICE RANGE: £150 to £200   PRICE RANGE: £30 to £50

FANCY WARES

PRICE RANGE: £45 to £75

PRICE RANGE: £120 to £180

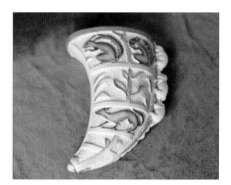

PRICE RANGE: £50 to £75

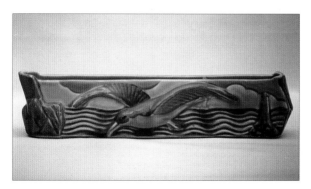

PRICE RANGE: £30 to £50

PRICE RANGE: £50 to £75

ALCOCK JUGS

FEEDING TIME
PRICE RANGE: £100 to £180

Courtesy of A & P Patterson

ALCOCK JUGS

NELL GWYN
PRICE RANGE: £100 to £180

Courtesy of D Bennett

RUNAWAY MARRIAGE
PRICE RANGE: £100 to £180

THE VILLAGE BLACKSMITH
Courtesy of A & P Patterson

DICKENS JUGS

Tony Weller, Sam Weller, Pickwick, Pecksniff   *Whole page courtesy of A & P Patterson*

Micawber, Scrooge, Oliver, Nicholas Nickelby

Sairey Gamp, Mrs Bardell   PRICE RANGE: £30 to £50

SHAKESPEARE JUGS

Portia and Wolsey

Whole page courtesy of A & P Patterson

Falstaff and A Midsummer Night's Dream

Macbeth and Caesar   PRICE RANGE: £30 to £50

WARTIME/CORONATION

WARTIME LEADERS
Jan Smuts, Winston Churchill, General MacArthur   *Courtesy of E Leigh*

CORONATION *and* BEEFEATER JUGS
PRICE RANGE: *£150 to £300*   *Courtesy of A & P Patterson*

Old Advertisement

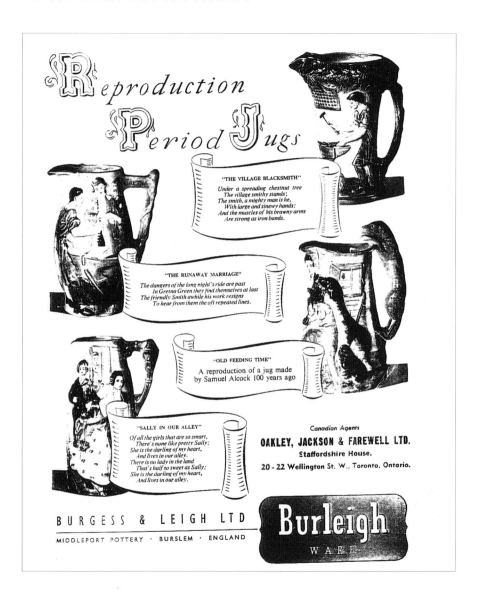

A page from "The Gift Buyer" showing the Alcock Jugs
Courtesy of Mr. E. Leigh

Price Guide

The prices in this guide for the yellow jugs and vases have been suggested for the most part by Lesley and Bill Jackson. Both have considerable experience in the buying and selling of Burleigh jugs and they are the proud owners of a fine collection. I am extremely grateful to them for their help with this. Prices are based on amounts realised at auctions, fairs, specialist and general shops and they represent average values. Since each item is worth what the buyer is prepared to pay, this can only be a guide. Prices are changing constantly and jugs which are scarce may well reach higher sums than shown. Values should be reduced on a sliding scale of up to 50% for anything more than minor damage or restoration.

A price guide for each jug has been included with its own photograph for easy reference.

The lowest prices are reserved for those jugs without the yellow glaze and with less desirable patterns. Rare jugs, fully hand painted attract the highest prices.

Unfinished Monkey & Cat showing visible flaw to rim
Courtesy of D Bennett

Backstamps

1930s   *1938 plus*

Conclusion

*I*t would seem from the many requests I have received to produce a guide to Jugs, that I was mistaken in the guide to Tableware when I stated in the Conclusion that the other Art Deco ceramics from this factory "have been well documented elsewhere". I sincerely hope that this publication will be well received and will prove useful and interesting to the many Burleigh collectors both here and abroad.

If anyone is interested in joining the newly formed Burleighware International Collectors Circle, or has further information or comments concerning this publication, they are most welcome to contact me via the publisher or at home:

Elizabeth Coupe
c/o Letterbox Publishing
Unit 1a Rural Industries
John O'Gaunt
Melton Mowbray
Leicestershire
LE14 2RE.

e-mail: THEBICC@aol.com

Elizabeth Coupe
9 Nursery Grove
Nettleham Road
Lincoln
LN2 1RS

Framed prints of the original artwork for the
cover illustrations by Deborah Hinks
may be purchased by sending a cheque for £15.00
made payable to Elizabeth Coupe
(to include postage and packing) to the above address.

Hemswell Antiques Centres

270 Shops in Three Adjacent Buildings
selling

Period Furniture — Shipping Furniture
Pine Furniture
Oriental Rugs — Long Case Clocks
Jewellery — Prints — Books — Silver
Pictures — Ceramics and many Collectables

Tel: Hemswell 668389
(STD 01427)

Open Daily 10.00a.m. to 5.00p.m.

10 Miles North of Lincoln
1 Mile from Caenby Corner
on the A631 to Gainsborough
Newark 25 Miles

Licensed Restaurant

Nationwide Deliveries arranged.
Container, Packing Service.
Single item shipping arranged.
Car Parking for 400 cars.

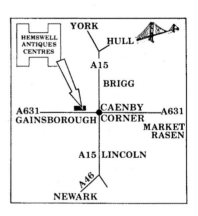

Hemswell Antiques Centres,
Caenby Corner Estate, Hemswell Cliff, Gainsborough, Lincs. DN21 5TJ.